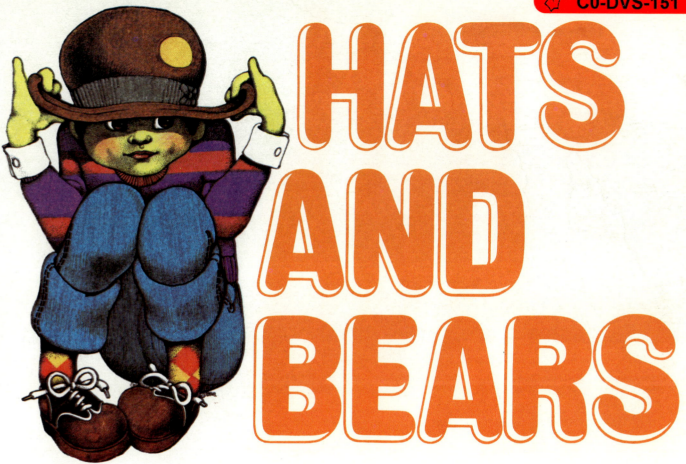

HATS AND BEARS

Florence Parry Heide
Sylvia Worth Van Clief

Macmillan Publishing Co., Inc.
New York
Collier Macmillan Publishers
London

Senior Authors
Carl B. Smith
Ronald Wardhaugh
Literature Consultant
Rudine Sims

Editor: *Kim Choi*
Art direction: *Zlata Paces*

ACKNOWLEDGMENTS

Pages 46-47 were written by Joyce Kennedy.

Illustrators: Ray Cruz, pp. 2-3; Errol LeCain, pp. 4-17; Marty Norman, pp. 18-19; Linda Gist, pp. 20-45; Don Almquist, pp. 46-47; Joanne Scribner, pp. 48-49; Ronald LeHew, pp. 50-63.

Cover Design: *Norman Gorbaty Design Inc.*

Macmillan Publishing Co., Inc.
866 Third Avenue, New York, N.Y. 10022
Collier-Macmillan Canada, Ltd.

Printed in the United States of America

Contents

Suzy paints a house.

"I don't like that.
It looks funny,"
says Bob.

"I like to paint funny things,"
says Suzy.

Suzy paints a pony
on the house.

"I don't like it.
It looks funny to see a pony
on a house,"
says Bob.

"I like funny things,"
says Suzy.

Suzy paints a fish
on the pony.

"I don't like it.
It looks funny to see a fish
on a pony,"
says Bob.

"I like funny things,"
says Suzy.

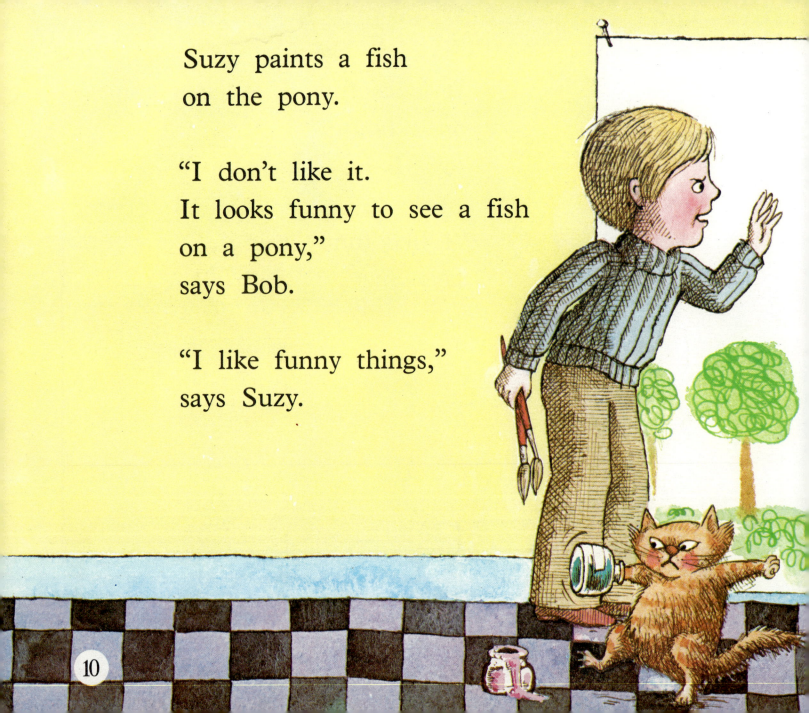

"A fish can't live
on a pony," says Bob.
"A fish likes to live
in a lake."
"A pony can't run
on a house," says Bob.
"A pony likes to run
in a park."

"I like funny things,"
says Suzy.

"I don't,"
says Bob.

13

Bob paints a house.
He paints a pony
in a park.
He paints a fish
in a lake.

Suzy sees the house,
the pony, and the fish.

"I don't like your house,
your pony, or your fish,"
says Suzy.
"I like funny things."

16

Standing in Line

Standing in line,
Standing in line,
Someone's ahead of me
Every time.
Someone's ahead
And someone's behind
Every time I'm standing in line!

Hats and Hats

21

24

Hats can't walk.
That hat is on a man.

25

The man likes hats.
Look.
He lives in a hat!

26

In and Out

We like your house.
And we like you.
Can we come in?

I like hats.
And I like you.
Come in.

29

30

I like your hats.
I like your house.
And I like you.
Can I come in?

I like hats.
And I like you.
Come in.

31

Look at that pony.
Look at that pony
in the funny hat.

I like your hat.

33

I can't.
The house is too little.

36

Is the house too little?
Or is the pony too big?

I like the house.
I like the house that is a hat.
But I like the pony, too.

Look at that red car.
Look at the man
and the birds
and the dog
and the pony in that red car.

And look at the funny hats.
Can we go, too?

40

We like birds.
And we like dogs.
You can come.
Jump in the car.

Look at that house.
Can we live in that house?

That house is too little.
We will go to the city.
We will live in a big house
in the city.

We like the house.
We like the house that is a hat.

TELL ABOUT

The Red Paint Pony

A Funny Hat

Little Lost Dog

The Big Fish

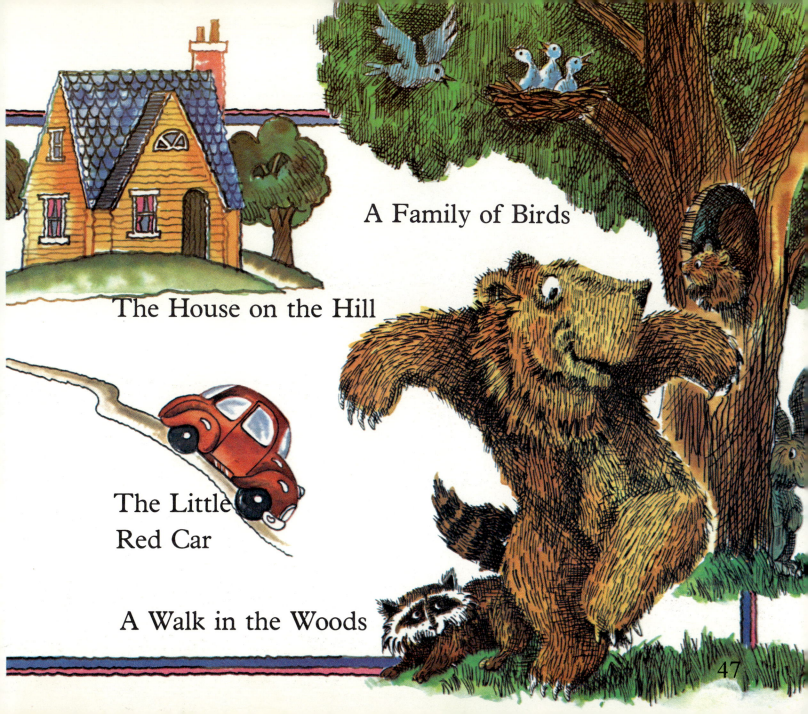

A Family of Birds

The House on the Hill

The Little
Red Car

A Walk in the Woods

47

HAT
ON MY
HEAD

Hat on my head,
Shoes on my feet,
That is the best way I've found.
I know it's true
Because I've tried
The other way around.

BIG
BEAR

Ben is a bear.
Ben is a big bear.
He likes to run
and jump.

Ben runs to the boys
and girls.
But then the boys and girls
run home.

Ben is sad.
Why is he sad?
The boys and girls
don't like Ben.

"Boys and girls can read,"
says Ben.
"I can read, too.
Then I can read
with the boys and girls.
Then I can run and jump
with the boys and girls."

But the boys and girls
don't read with Ben.
The boys and girls
run home.

The Party

The boys and girls
have a party.

"Boys and girls like
presents," Ben says.
"I have a present.
I can come to the party.
The boys and girls
will like the present.
Then the boys and girls
will like me."

Ben does have a present.
But the boys and girls
don't like Ben.

58

Ben sits.
And Ben sits.
He is sad.
"The boys and girls
don't like me,"
he says.
Then it rains.
It rains and rains.

59

Ben looks at the present.
What is it?
What is the present?
The present is
a big umbrella.

60

It rains and rains.
It rains
on the boys and girls.
It rains on the umbrella.

61

The boys and girls see Ben
and the umbrella.
The boys and girls run.

The boys and girls run
to Ben and the umbrella.
The boys and girls have
a party with Ben.
The boys and girls like Ben.

Ben says,
"I like the boys and girls,
and the boys and girls like me!"

WORD LIST

The new words introduced in this book are listed below beside the page number on which they first appear. The children should be able to independently identify italicized words at this level.

7.	Suzy	40.	red
	paints	50.	bear
	don't	52.	Ben
	it	53.	then
	looks	54.	sad
	paint	55.	with
8.	on	57.	party
21.	hats		presents
22.	hat		*present*
	have		me
26.	*lives*	59.	rains
28.	come	60.	umbrella
30.	at		
39.	will		
	go		
	country		